Landscapes
colour by numbers

Landscapes
colour by numbers

Martin Sanders and David Woodroffe

ARCTURUS

ARCTURUS

This edition published in 2018 by Arcturus Publishing Limited
26/27 Bickels Yard, 151–153 Bermondsey Street,
London SE1 3HA

ISBN: 978-1-78428-767-2
CH005580NT
Supplier 29, Date 1217, Print Run 6217

Printed in China
Created for children aged 10+

INTRODUCTION

The earth's landscapes are some of its greatest wonders. From sun-seared deserts and freezing mountains where only the toughest survive, to coral reefs and rainforests swarming with life, landscapes are fascinating in their variety. This collection of colour-by-number landscapes reflects that diversity, showing coastal views, dramatic waterfalls and mountains, safari scenes and bucolic country panoramas. Some images portray the impact of man on the landscape, such as the beautiful rice paddies carved out of a Chinese mountainside or the ancient stone circle at Stonehenge; others show wild places like the Antarctic or salmon jumping in a North American river. You will also find landscapes that are instantly recognizable, like Mount Fuji, Ayers Rock and Niagara Falls.

Each image is fully numbered so that, by following the key on the back cover flap, you can build up an impressive landscape scene. Match your pencils as closely as possible to the colours in the key – you can even label the pencils with numbers to make things easier. If there is no number that means the space should be left white or coloured with a white pencil.

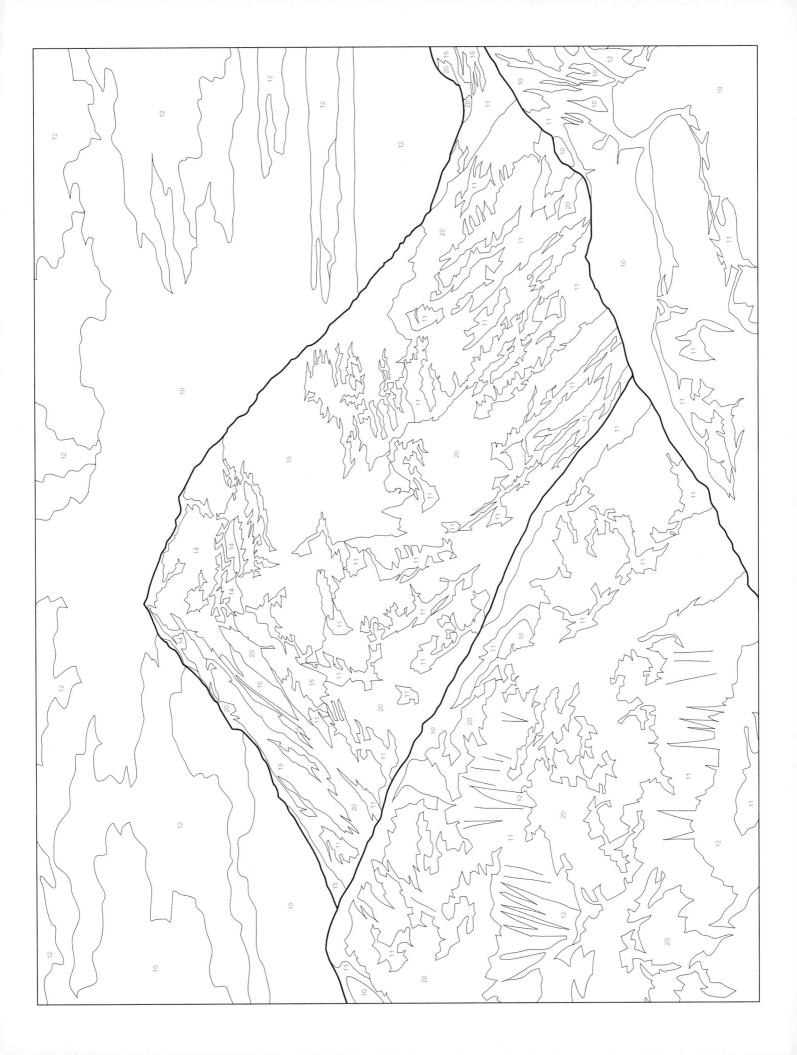

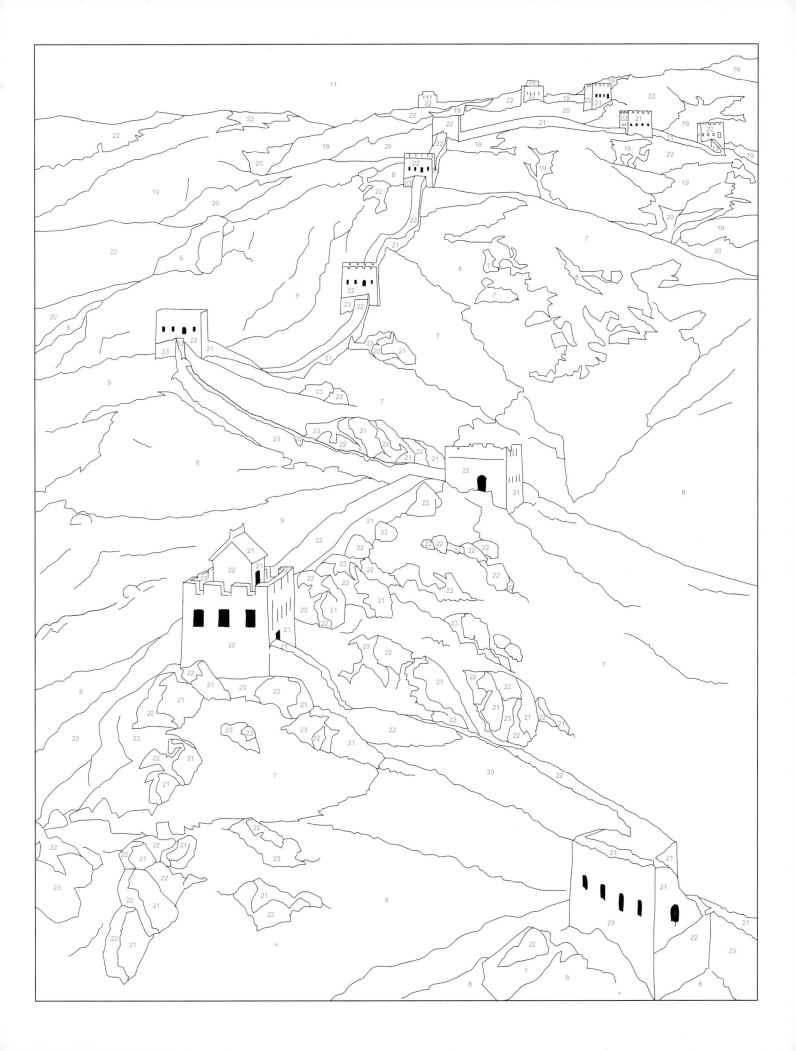

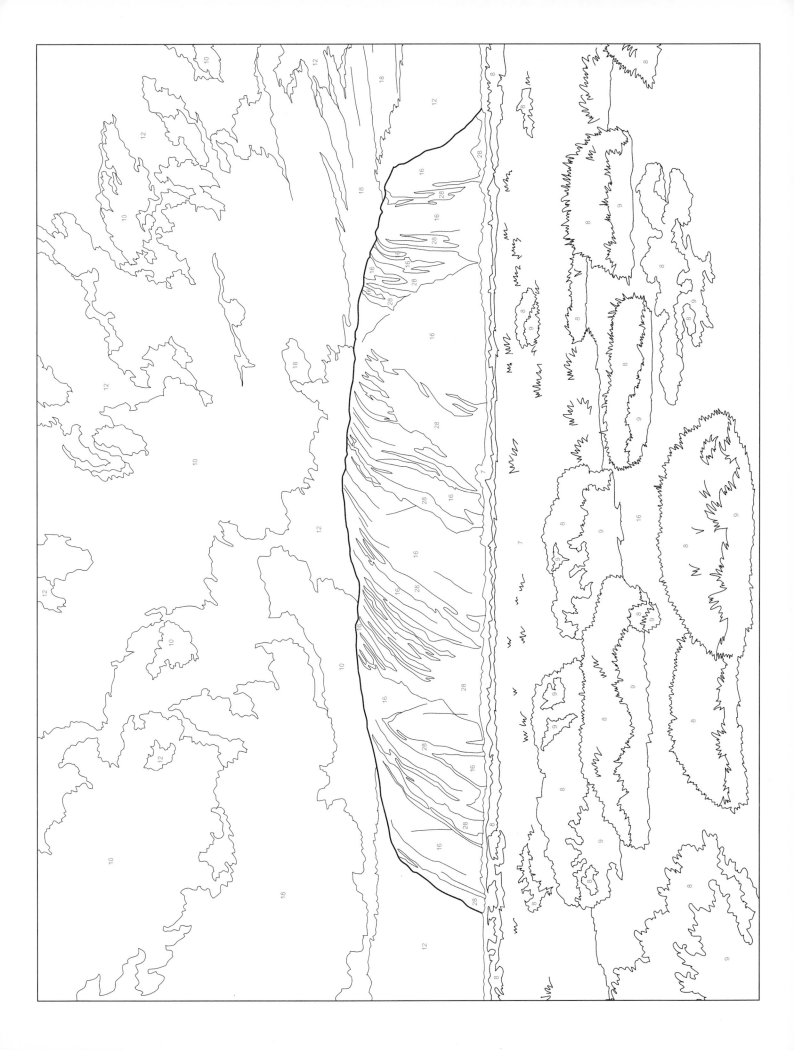

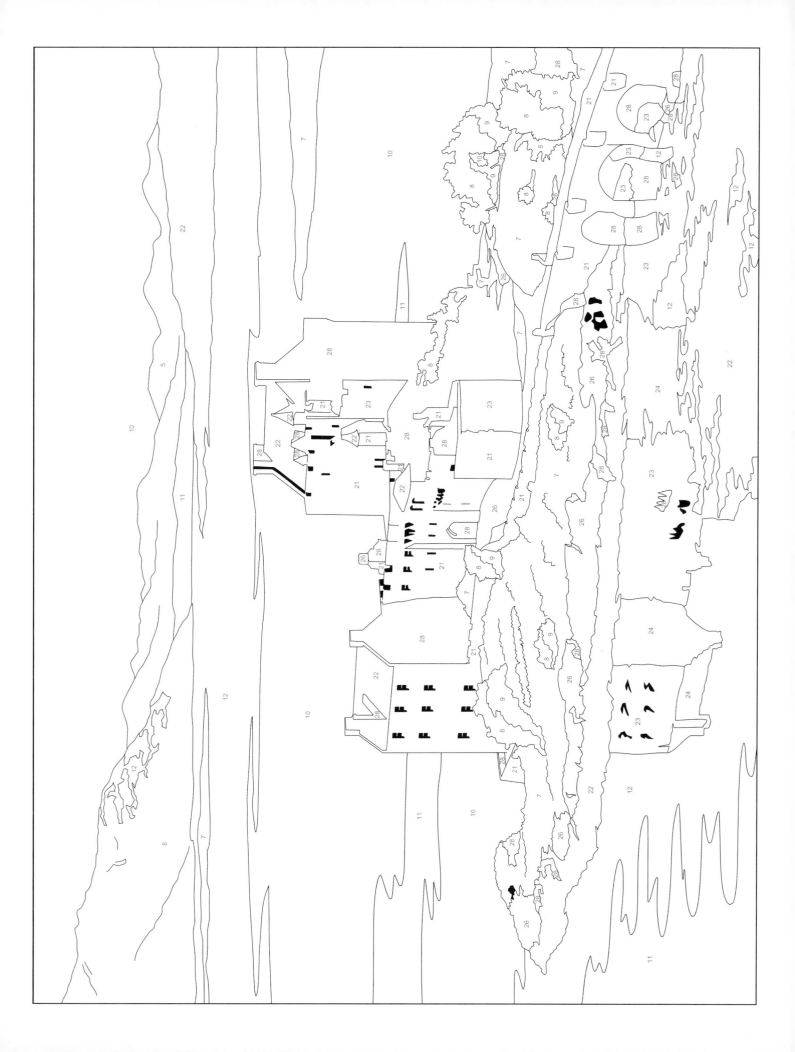

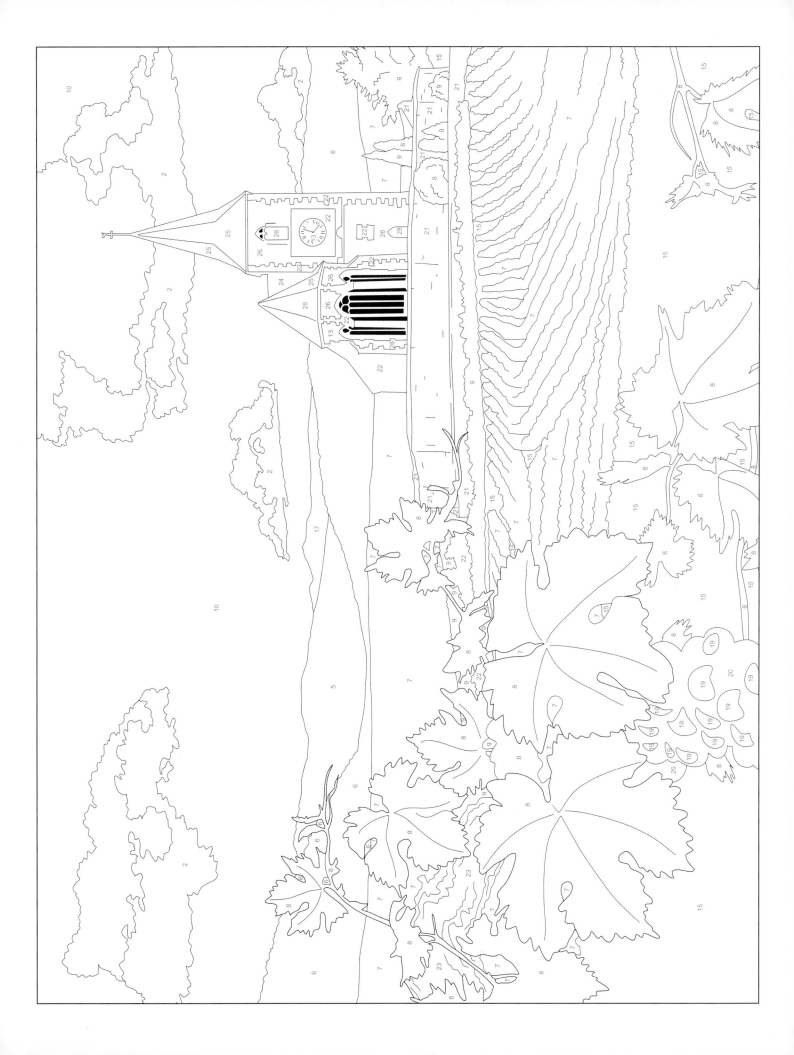

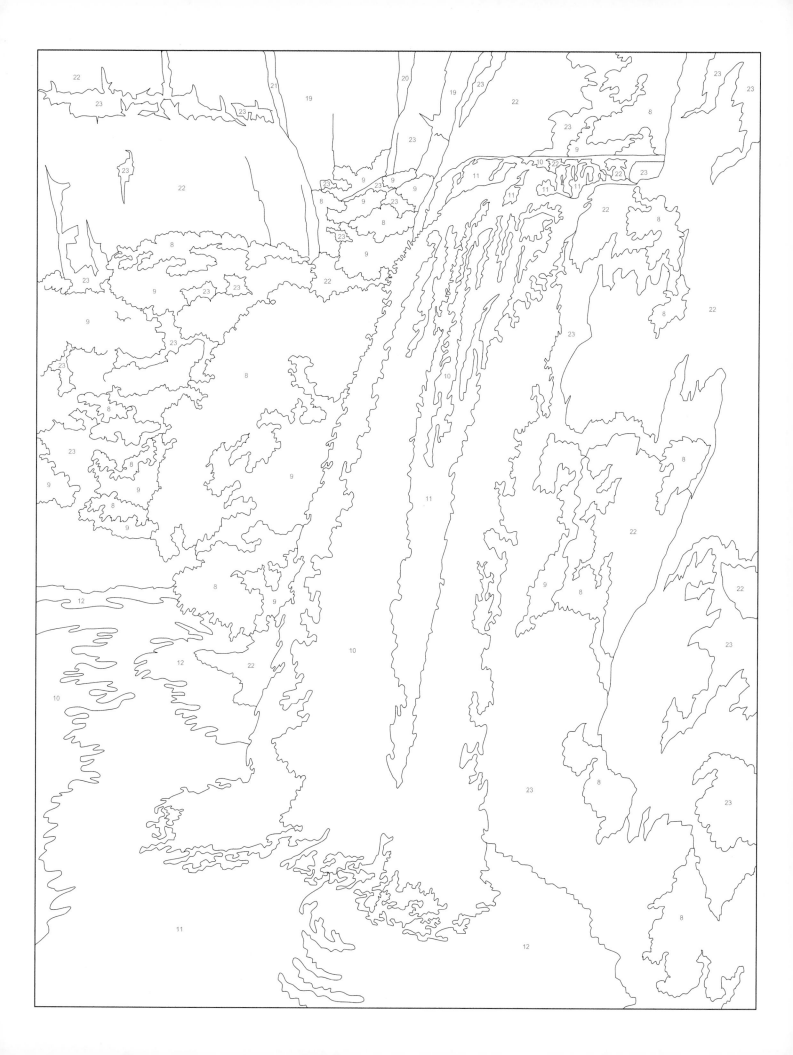

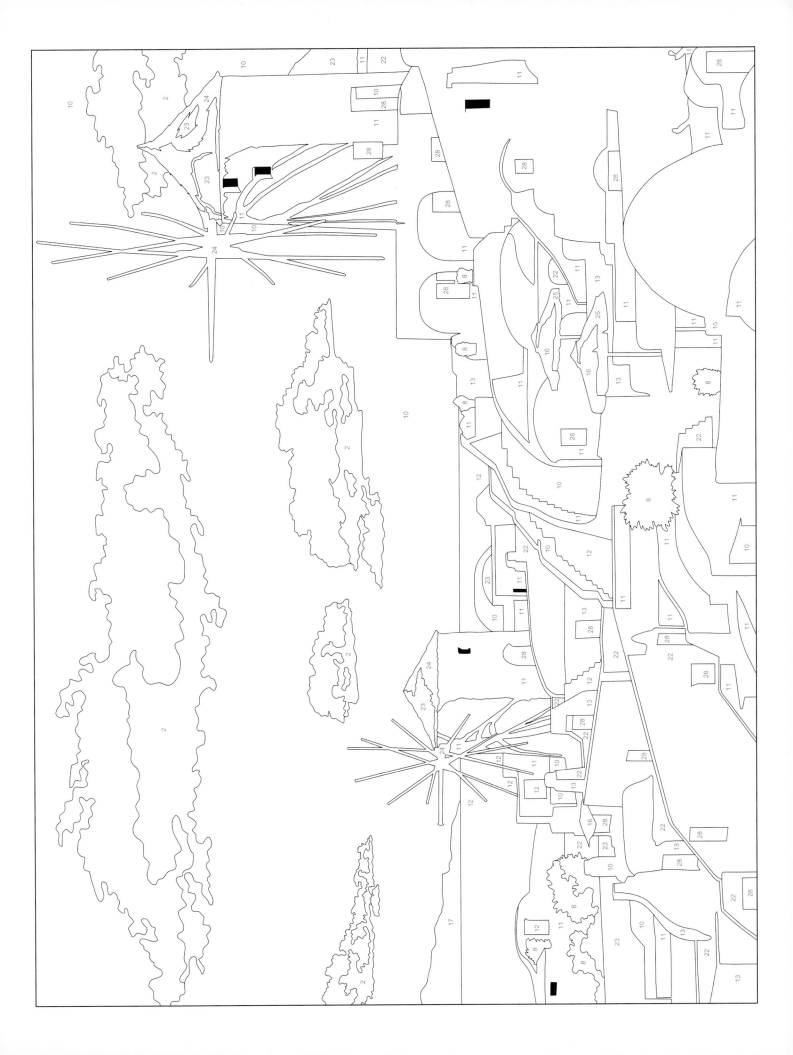

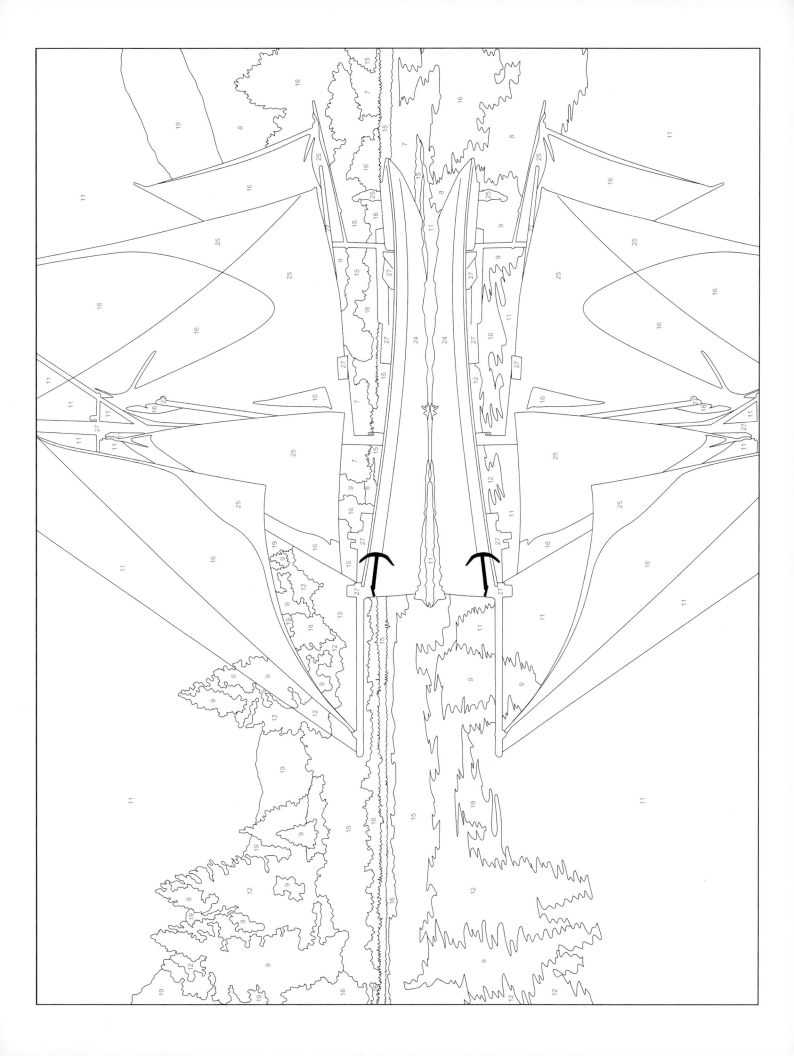

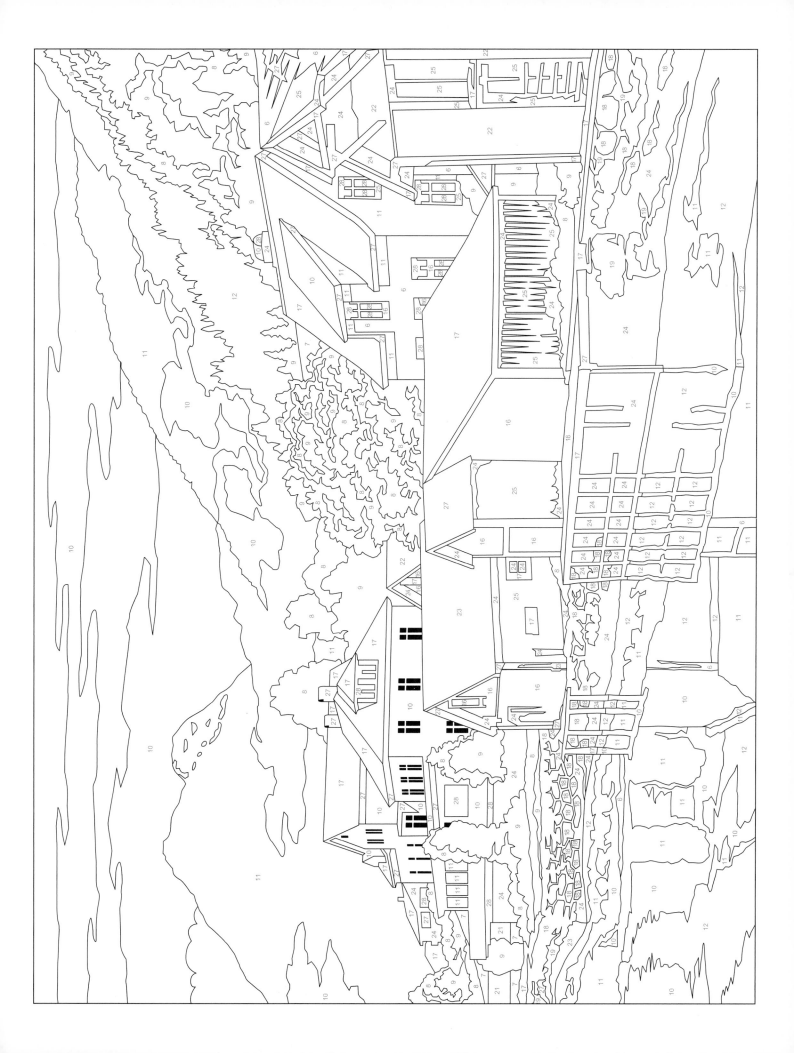

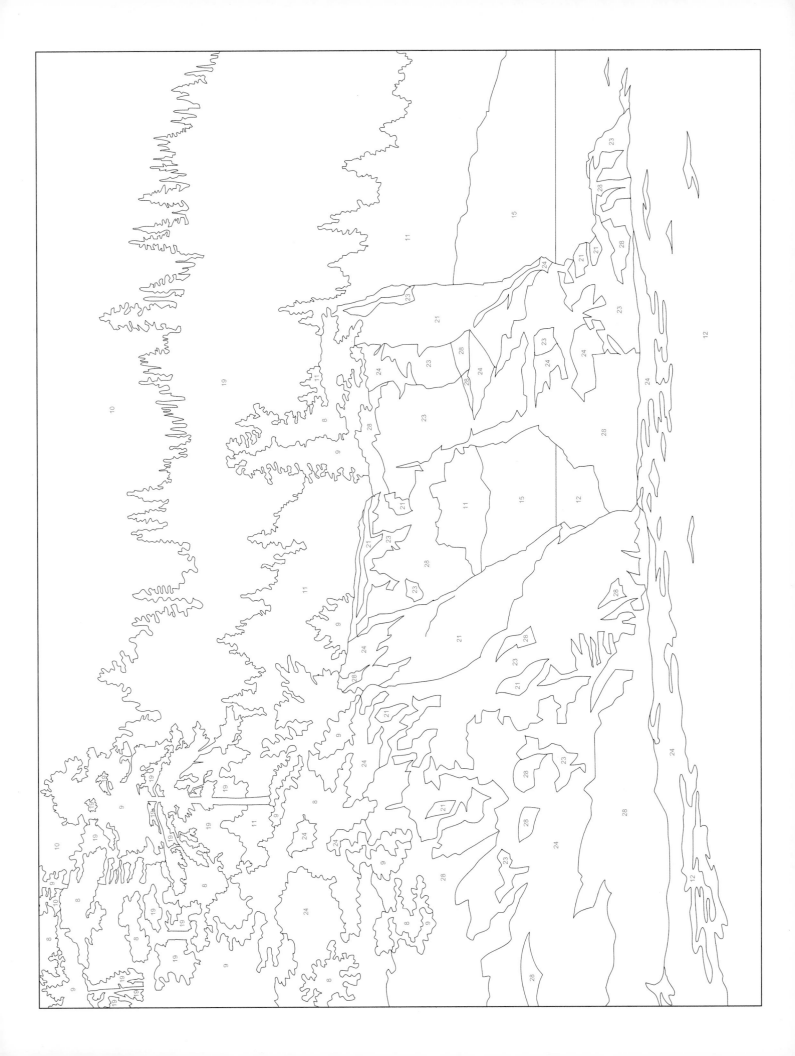

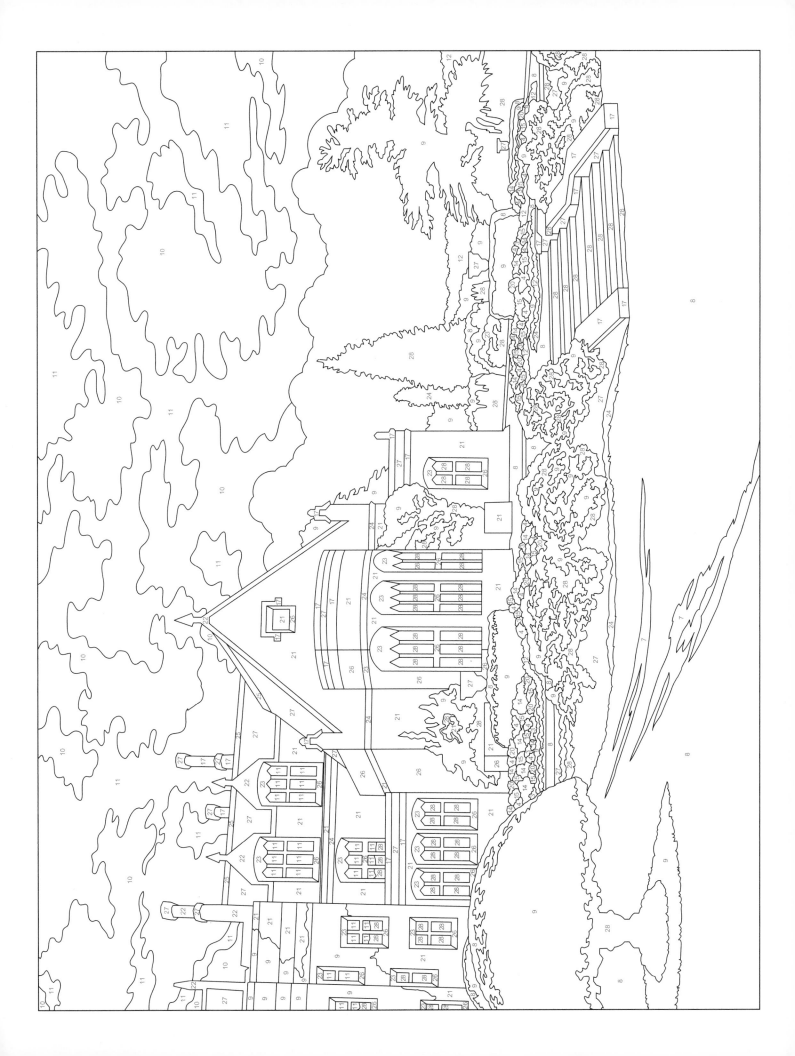

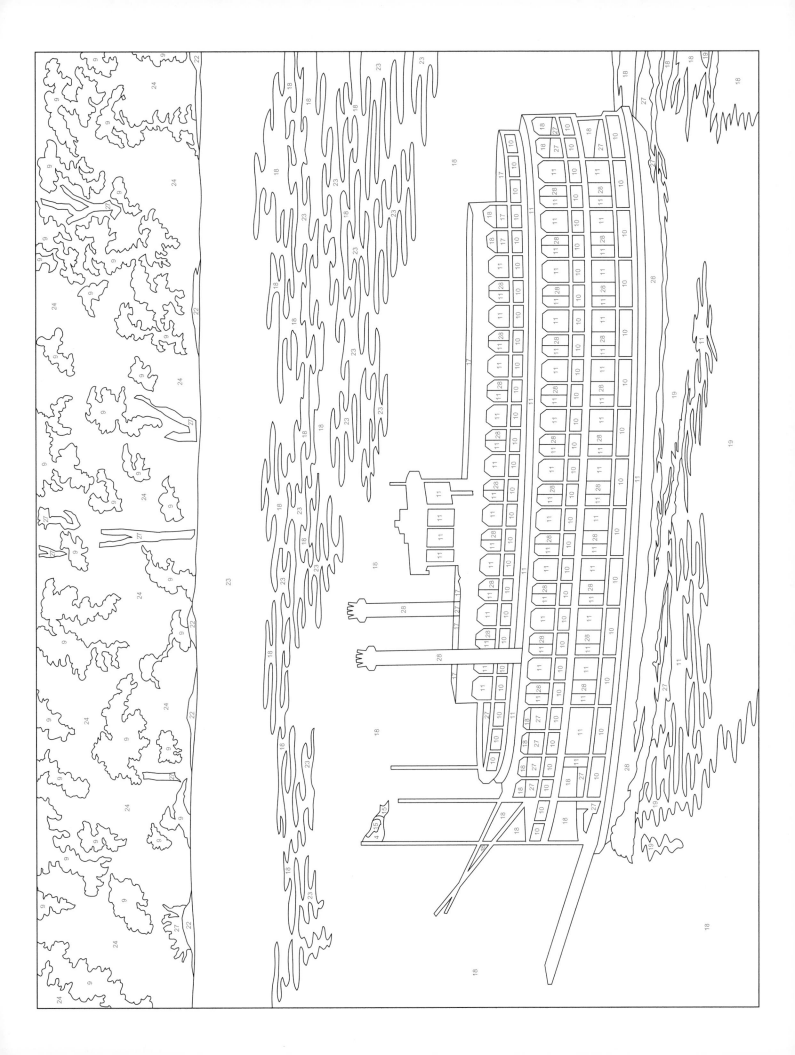

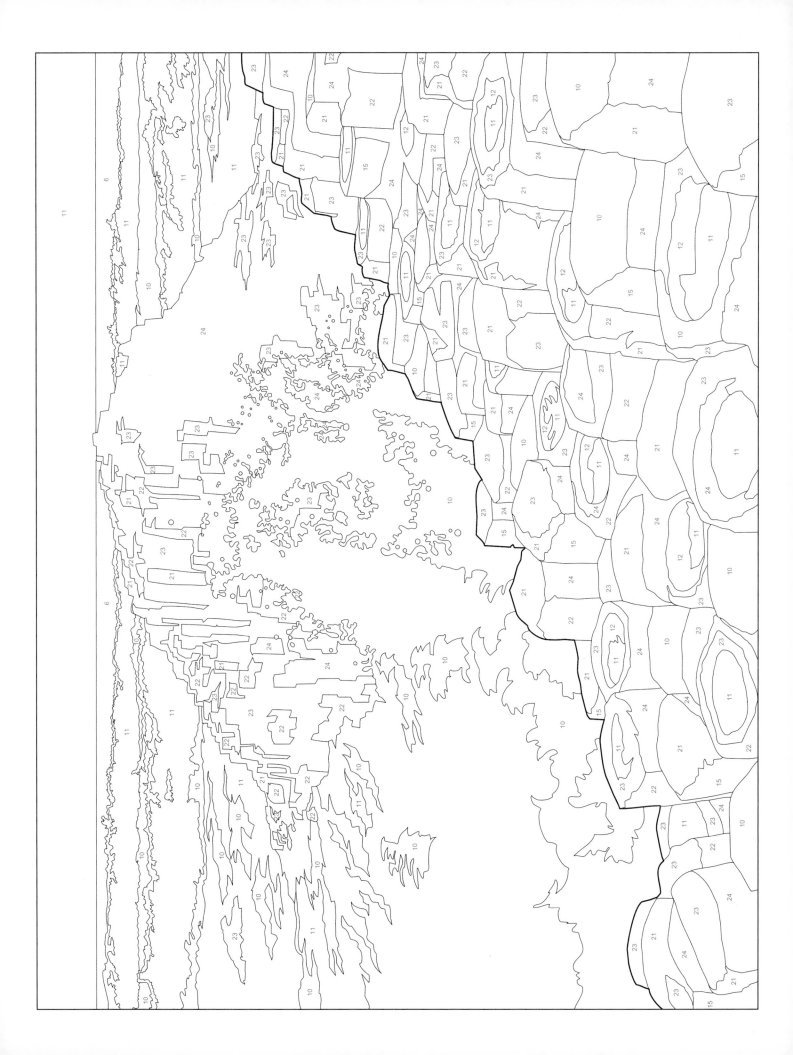

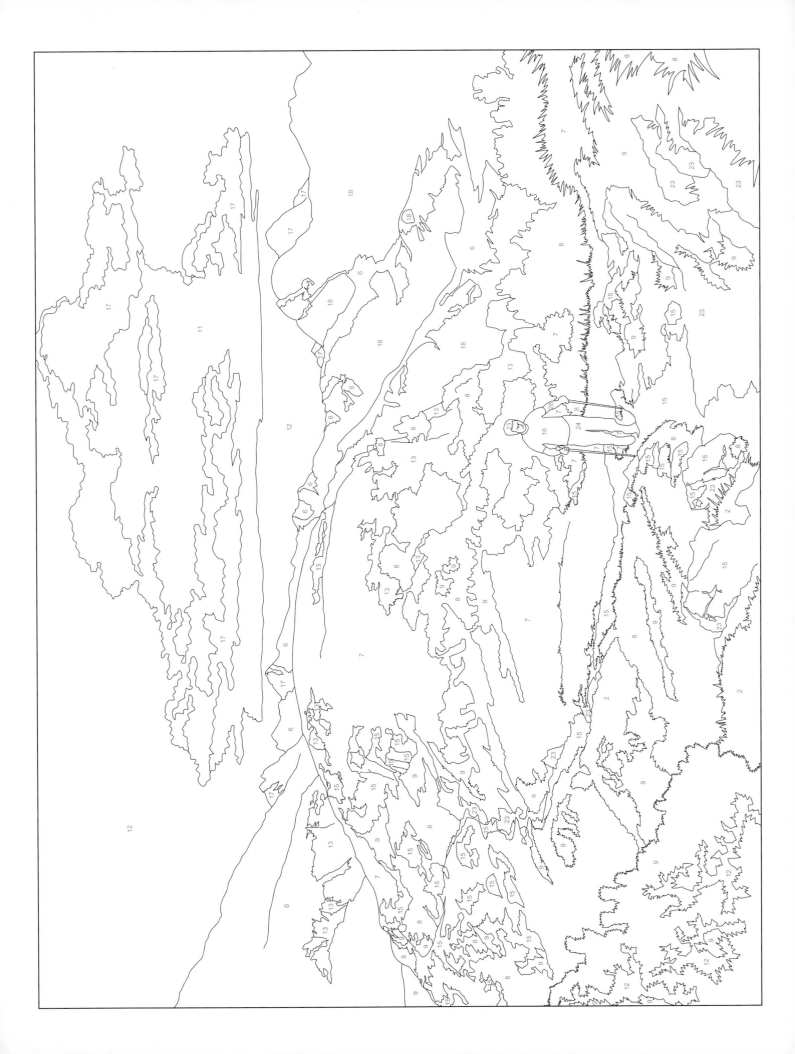

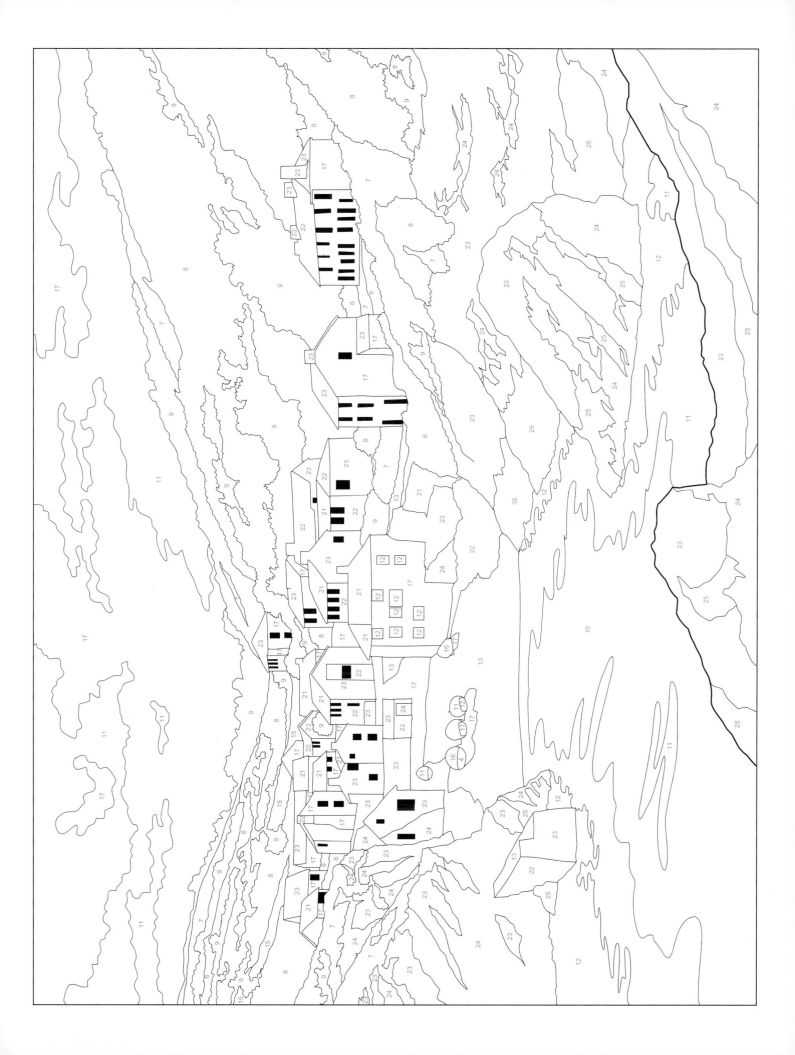

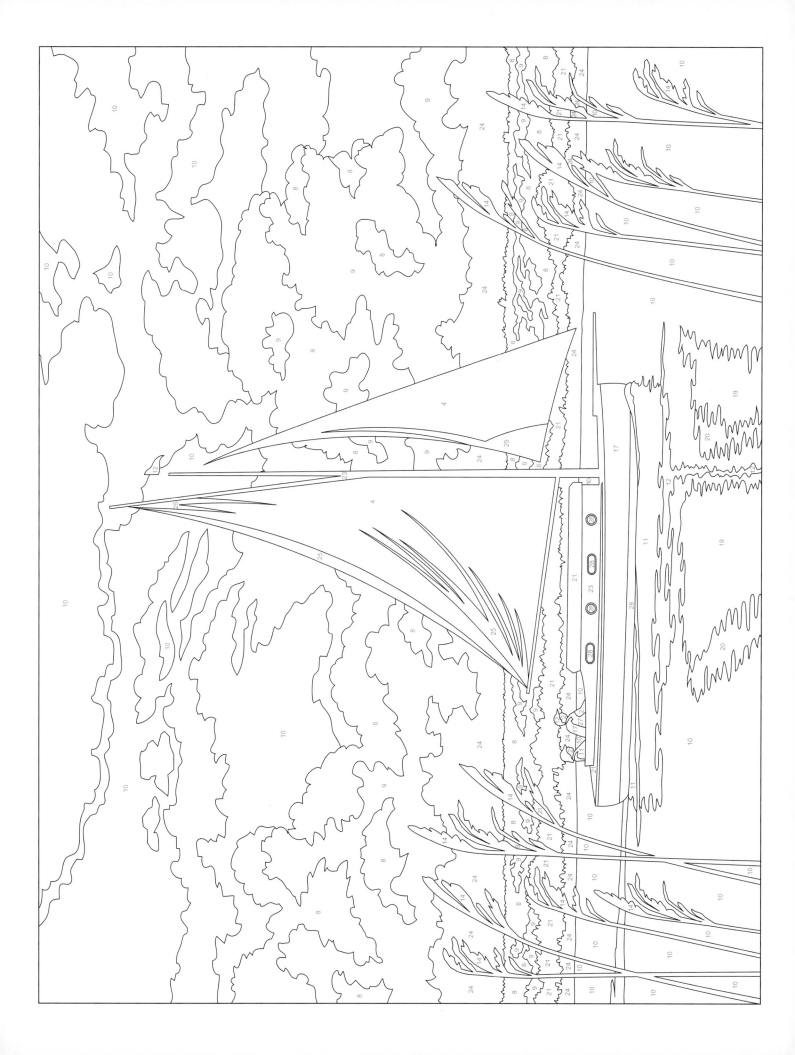

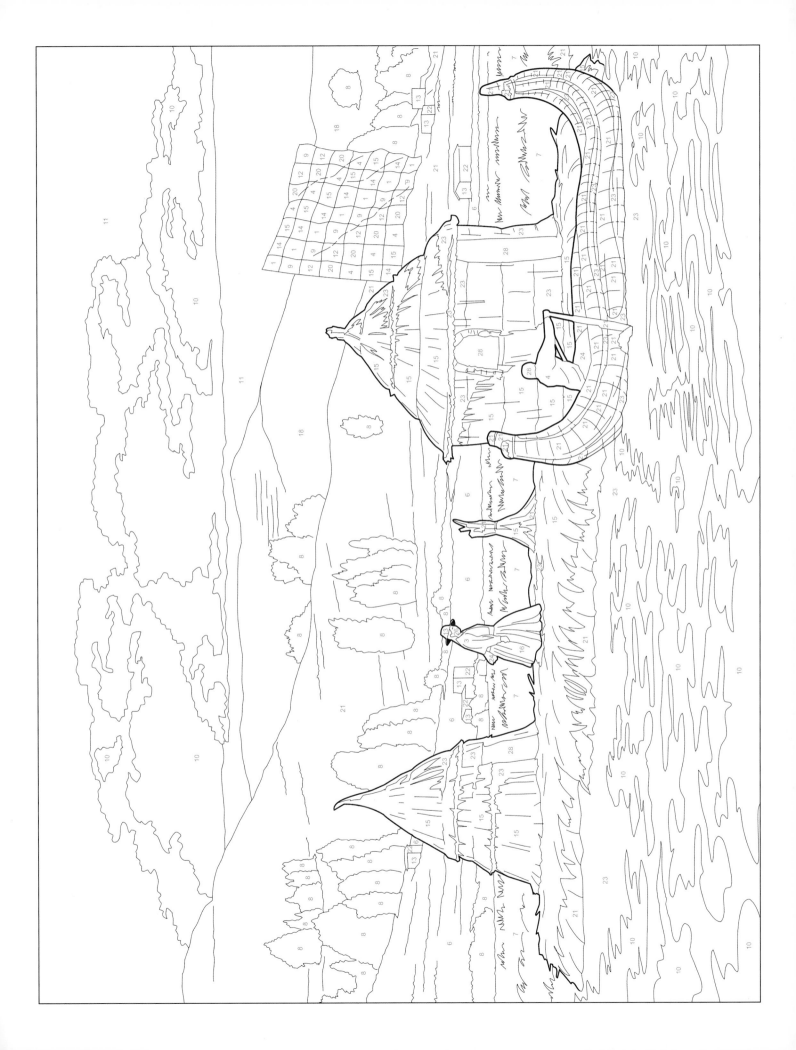

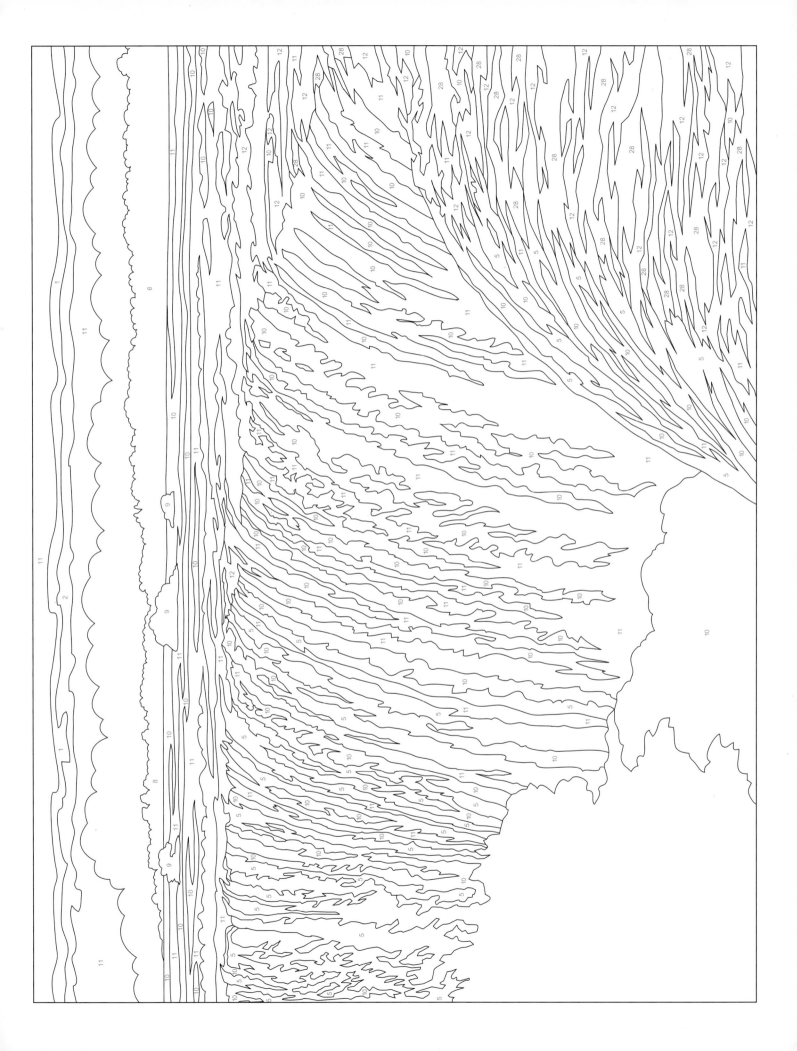